Guitar
Scales & Exercises

for Trinity Guildhall Guitar
& Plectrum Guitar examinations
from 2007

Initial-Grade 8

Published by:
Trinity College London
89 Albert Embankment
London SE1 7TP UK

T +44 (0)20 7820 6100
F +44 (0)20 7820 6161
E music@trinityguildhall.co.uk
www.trinityguildhall.co.uk

Printed in England by Halstan & Co. Ltd, Amersham, Bucks.

Guitar Initial

Scales and arpeggio (♩ = 60):

The following scales to be performed *legato*, ***mf***, with *im* right-hand fingering unless otherwise stated. Candidate's choice of *apoyando* or *tirando* unless specified:

C major (to 5th, ascending and descending)

G major (to 5th, ascending and descending)

A minor (to 5th, ascending and descending)

Phrygian starting on E (one octave, ascending and descending with RH thumb) (*tirando*)

The following arpeggio to be performed *legato*, ***mf***:

D minor (to 5th, ascending and descending) (*tirando*)

C major scale (to 5th)

G major scale (to 5th)

A minor scale (to 5th)

Phrygian scale starting on E (one octave)

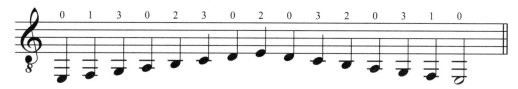

D minor arpeggio (to 5th)

Guitar Grade 1

Scales (♩ = 100):

The following scales to be performed *legato*, *mf*, with *im* right-hand fingering unless otherwise stated. Candidate's choice of *apoyando* or *tirando* unless specified:

C major (one octave)
G major (one octave)
F major (one octave, with RH thumb) (*tirando*)
Dorian starting on D (one octave)

Arpeggios (♩ = 80):

The following arpeggios to be performed *legato*, *mf*, with right-hand fingering *pimamip*:

C major (one octave) (*tirando*)
E minor (one octave) (*tirando*)

C major scale (one octave)

G major scale (one octave)

F major scale (one octave)

Dorian scale starting on D (one octave)

C major arpeggio (one octave)

E minor arpeggio (one octave)

Guitar Grade 2

Scales (♩ = 126):

The following scales to be performed *legato*, with the dynamics shown and with *im* right-hand fingering unless otherwise stated. Candidate's choice of *apoyando* or *tirando* unless specified:

C major (one octave), *mf*
D major (one octave), *p*
A natural minor (one octave), *mf*
A harmonic minor (one octave), *p*
A melodic minor (one octave), *mf*

Arpeggios (♩ = 100):

The following arpeggios to be performed *legato*, *mf*, and *tirando*:

E minor (one octave with RH thumb)
Arpeggiated D major chord sequence ii-V-I: right-hand fingering based on *pima*

C major scale (one octave)

D major scale (one octave)

A natural minor scale (one octave)

A harmonic minor scale (one octave)

A melodic minor scale (one octave)

Grade 2 continued

E minor arpeggio (one octave)

Arpeggiated D major chord sequence (one octave)

Guitar Grade 3

Scales (♩ = 72):

The following scales to be performed *legato* with dynamics, right-hand fingering pattern and rhythmic style as listed below. Candidates choice of *apoyando* or *tirando* unless specified:

C major (two octaves), *mf*, *ma* fingering. Straight rhythm

D natural minor (two octaves), *p*, *ma* fingering. Straight rhythm

D harmonic minor (two octaves), *mf*, *im* fingering. Swing rhythm

D melodic minor (two octaves). *p*, *im* fingering. Swing rhythm

Arpeggio (♩ = 60):

The following arpeggio to be performed *legato*, *mf*, and *tirando*:

Diminished 7th starting on A (one octave)

Exercises:

The following exercises to be performed *legato*, *mf*, and *tirando*:

C major scale in broken thirds (♩ = 72)

Half barré in A minor (♪ = 120)

C major scale (two octaves)

D natural minor scale (two octaves)

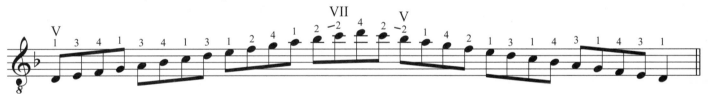

D harmonic minor scale (two octaves)

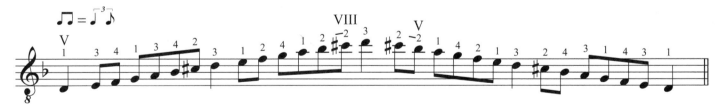

D melodic minor scale (two octaves)

Grade 3 continued

Diminished 7th arpeggio starting on A

C major scale in broken thirds (one octave)

Half barré in A minor

Guitar Grade 4

Scales (♩ = 84):

The following scales to be performed *legato*, with dynamics, right-hand fingering pattern and rhythmic style as listed below. Candidate's choice of *apoyando* or *tirando* unless specified:

A major (two octaves), **f**, *im* fingering. Straight rhythm

E major (two octaves), **mf**, *im* fingering. Straight rhythm

B natural minor (two octaves), **p**, *ma* fingering. Straight rhythm

B harmonic minor (two octaves), **f**, *ma* fingering. Swing rhythm

B melodic minor (two octaves), **p**, *ma* fingering. Swing rhythm

Arpeggios (♪ = 108):

The following arpeggios to be performed, *legato*, **mf** and *tirando*:

D major (two octaves)

B minor (two octaves)

Dominant 7th in the key of D (two octaves, starting on A)

A major scale (two octaves)

E major scale (two octaves)

B natural minor (two octaves)

B harmonic minor scale (two octaves)

Grade 4 continued

B melodic minor scale (two octaves)

D major arpeggio (two octaves)

B minor arpeggio (two octaves)

Dominant 7th arpeggio in the key of D (two octaves)

Guitar Grade 5

Scales (♩ = 96):

The following scales to be performed *legato*, with dynamics, right-hand fingering pattern, rhythmic style and tone as listed below.

To be played *apoyando*:

F major (two octaves), *f*, *ma* fingering. Straight rhythm, *norm.* tone

B♭ major (two octaves), *f*, *ma* fingering. Straight rhythm, *norm.* tone

Chromatic starting on E (three octaves), *f*, *im* fingering. Swing rhythm, *pont.* tone

To be played *tirando*:

F♯ natural minor (two octaves), *mf*, *ma* fingering. Swing rhythm, *pont.* tone

F♯ harmonic minor (two octaves), *mf*, *ma* fingering. Swing rhythm, *pont.* tone

F♯ melodic minor (two octaves), *mf*, *ma* fingering. Swing rhythm, *pont.* tone

C major pentatonic (two octaves), *p*, *im* fingering. Straight rhythm, *norm.* tone

Arpeggios (♪ = 120):

The following arpeggios to be performed *legato*, *mf* and *tirando*:

B♭ major (two octaves)

Dominant 7th in the key of E♭ (two octaves, starting on B♭)

Exercises:

The following exercises to be performed *legato*, *mf* and *tirando*:

Paired slurs in A major (♩ = 72)

B♭ major in thirds (♩ = 72)

Full barré sequence (♩. = 60)

F major scale (two octaves)

B♭ major scale (two octaves)

Grade 5 continued

Chromatic scale on E (three octaves)

F# natural minor scale (two octaves)

F# harmonic minor scale (two octaves)

F# melodic minor scale (two octaves)

C major pentatonic scale (two octaves)

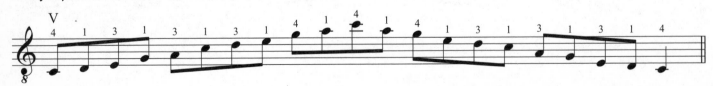

B♭ major arpeggio (two octaves)

Dominant 7th arpeggio in the key of E♭ (two octaves)

Paired slurs in A major (one octave)

B♭ major scale in thirds (one octave)

Full barré sequence

Guitar Grade 6

Scales (♩ = 100):

The following scales to be performed *legato* with dynamics, right-hand fingering pattern, rhythmic style and tone as listed below.

To be played *apoyando*:

G major (three octaves), ***f***, *imam* fingering. Straight rhythm, *norm.* tone

C major (two octaves), ***f***, *imam* fingering. Straight rhythm, *norm.* tone

G melodic minor (three octaves), ***p***, *imam* fingering. Swing rhythm, *pont.* tone

C melodic minor (two octaves), ***p***, *imam* fingering. Swing rhythm, *pont.* tone

To be played *tirando*:

G natural minor (three octaves), ***mf***, *ma* fingering. Swing rhythm, *pont.* tone

C natural minor (two octaves), ***mf***, *ma* fingering. Swing rhythm, *pont.* tone

G harmonic minor (three octaves), ***f***, *im* fingering. Triplet rhythm, *norm.* tone

C harmonic minor (two octaves), ***f***, *im* fingering. Triplet rhythm, *norm.* tone

Arpeggios (♩. = 80):

The following arpeggios to be performed *legato*, ***mf*** and *tirando*:

G major (three octaves)

C major (two octaves)

G minor (three octaves)

C minor (two octaves)

Dominant 7th in the key of C (three octaves, starting on G)

Dominant 7th in the key of F (two octaves, starting on C)

Diminished 7th starting on G (three octaves)

Diminished 7th starting on C (two octaves)

Exercises (♩ = 84):

The following exercises to be performed *legato*, ***mf*** and *tirando*:

C major scale in thirds (two octaves)

G major scale in thirds (two octaves)

Chromatic scale in octaves starting on C (one octave)

Chromatic scale in octaves starting on G (one octave)

G major scale (three octaves)

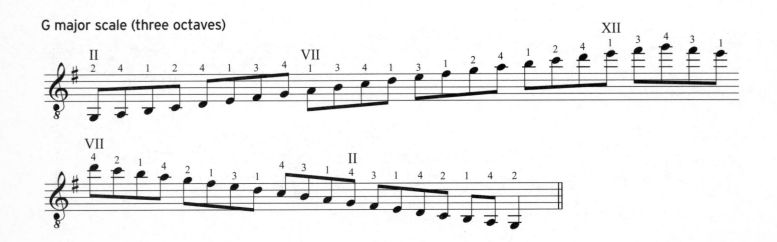

C major scale (two octaves)

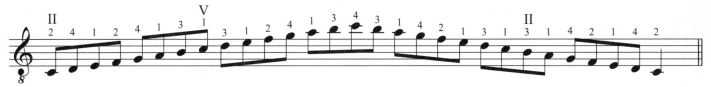

G melodic minor scale (three octaves)

C melodic minor scale (two octaves)

G natural minor scale (three octaves)

C natural minor scale (two octaves)

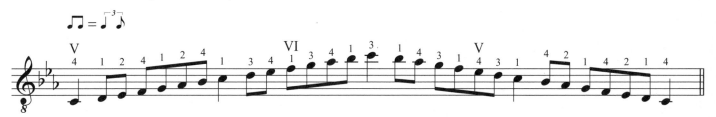

Guitar Grade 6 continued

G harmonic minor scale (three octaves)

C harmonic minor scale (two octaves)

G major arpeggio (three octaves)

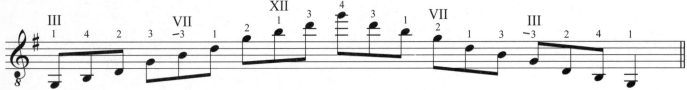

C major arpeggio (two octaves)

G minor arpeggio (three octaves)

C minor arpeggio (two octaves)

Dominant 7th arpeggio in the key of C (three octaves)

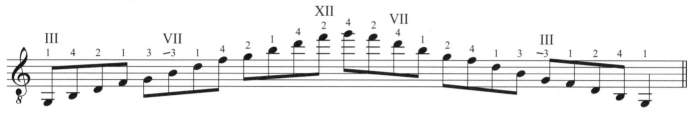

Dominant 7th arpeggio in the key of F (two octaves)

Diminished 7th arpeggio on G (three octaves)

Diminished 7th arpeggio on C (two octaves)

C major scale in thirds (two octaves)

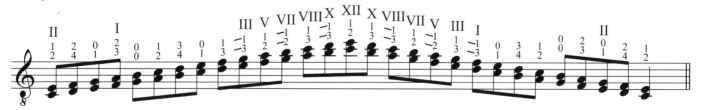

Guitar Grade 6 continued

G major scale in thirds (two octaves)

Chromatic scale in octaves starting on C (one octave)

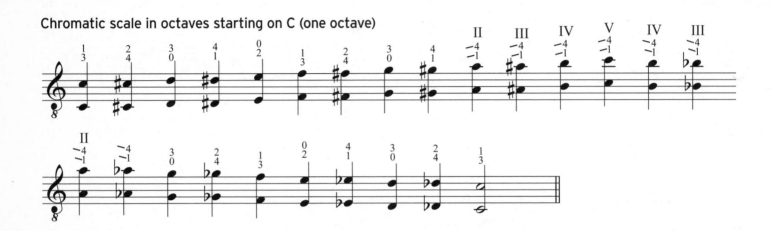

Chromatic scale in octaves starting on G (one octave)

Guitar Grade 7

Scales (♩ = 112):

The following scales to be performed with dynamics, right-hand fingering pattern, rhythmic style and tone as listed below.

To be played *apoyando* and *staccato*:

A major (three octaves), *mf*, *imam* fingering. Straight rhythm, *norm.* tone
D major (two octaves), *mf*, *imam* fingering. Straight rhythm, *norm.* tone

To be played *apoyando* and *legato*:

A melodic minor (three octaves), *p*, *imam* fingering. Swing rhythm, *pont.* tone
D melodic minor (two octaves), *p*, *imam* fingering. Swing rhythm, *pont.* tone

To be played *tirando* and *legato*, with tone colour gradually changing from *norm.* to *pont.* to *norm.* again:

A natural minor (three octaves), *f*, *ma* fingering. Swing rhythm
D natural minor (two octaves), *f*, *ma* fingering. Swing rhythm

To be played *tirando* and *legato*:

A harmonic minor (three octaves), *mf*, *im* fingering. Triplet rhythm, *pont.* tone
D harmonic minor (two octaves), *mf*, *im* fingering. Triplet rhythm, *pont.* tone

To be played *tirando* and *staccato*:

A major pentatonic (three octaves), *f*, *im* fingering. Straight rhythm, *norm.* tone
D major pentatonic (two octaves), *f*, *im* fingering. Straight rhythm, *norm.* tone

To be played *apoyando* and *legato*:

Mixolydian starting on A (three octaves), *p*, *ma* fingering. Triplet rhythm, *norm.* tone
Mixolydian starting on D (two octaves), *p*, *ma* fingering. Triplet rhythm, *tasto* tone

Arpeggios (♩. = 92):

The following arpeggios to be performed *legato* and *tirando*:

A major (three octaves), *f*, *pont.* tone
D major (two octaves), *f*, *pont.* tone
A minor (three octaves), *p*, *norm.* tone
D minor (two octaves), *p*, *tasto* tone
Dominant 7th in the key of D (three octaves, starting on A), *mf*
Dominant 7th in the key of G (two octaves, starting on D), *mf*
Diminished 7th starting on A (three octaves), *mf*
Diminished 7th starting on D (two octaves), *mf*

Exercises (♩. = 96):

The following exercises to be performed *legato*, *mf* and *tirando*:
D major scale in paired slurs (two octaves)
A major scale in 3rds (two octaves)
D harmonic minor scale in 6ths (two octaves)
A melodic minor scale in octaves (two octaves)

Guitar Grade 7 continued

A major scale (three octaves)

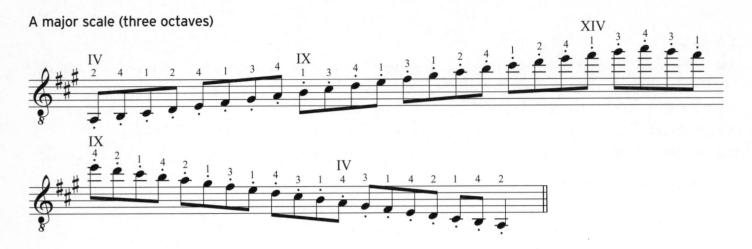

D major scale (two octaves)

A melodic minor scale (three octaves)

D melodic minor scale (two octaves)

A natural minor scale (three octaves)

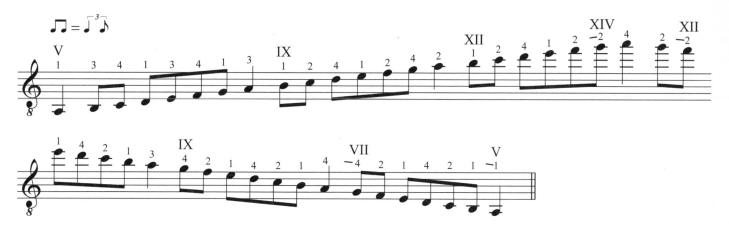

D natural minor scale (two octaves)

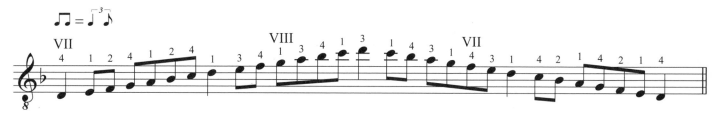

A harmonic minor scale (three octaves)

D harmonic minor scale (two octaves)

Guitar Grade 7 continued

A major pentatonic scale (three octaves)

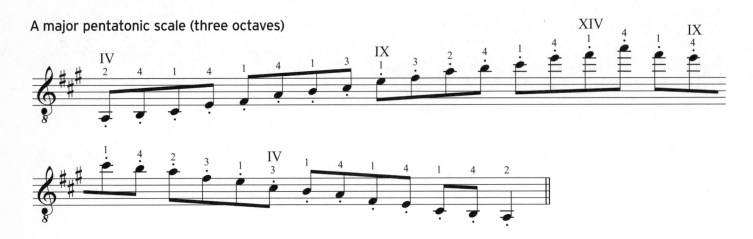

D major pentatonic scale (two octaves)

Mixolydian scale on starting on A (three octaves)

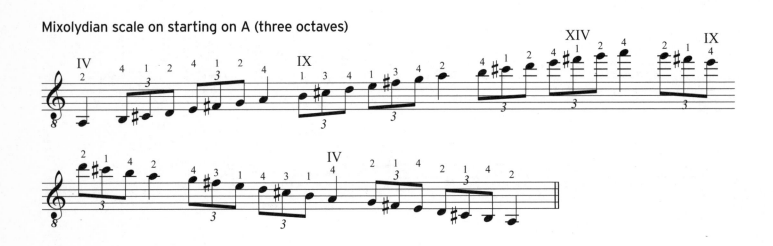

Mixolydian scale starting on D (two octaves)

A major arpeggio (three octaves)

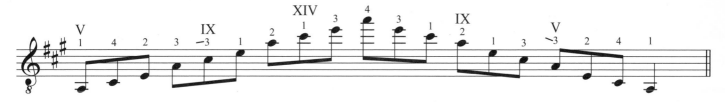

D major arpeggio (two octaves)

A minor arpeggio (three octaves)

D minor arpeggio (two octaves)

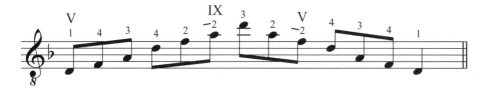

Dominant 7th arpeggio in D (three octaves)

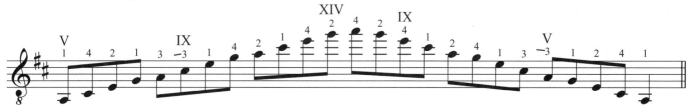

Guitar Grade 7 continued

Dominant 7th arpeggio in G (two octaves)

Diminished 7th arpeggio starting on A (three octaves)

Diminished 7th arpeggio starting on D (two octaves)

D major scale in paired slurs (two octaves)

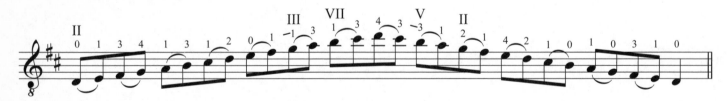

A major scale in 3rds (two octaves)

D harmonic minor scale in 6ths (two octaves)

A melodic minor scale in octaves (two octaves)

Guitar Grade 8

Scales (♩ = 126):

The following scales to be performed with dynamics, right-hand fingering pattern, rhythmic style and tone as listed below. Scales based on F must be played starting on the fifth string.

To be played *tirando* and *legato*, *cresc.* ascending and *dim.* descending:

Bb major (three octaves), *im* fingering. Straight rhythm, *norm.* tone
F major (two octaves), *im* fingering. Straight rhythm, *norm.* tone

To be played *tirando* and *staccato*:

Bb harmonic minor (three octaves), *mf*, *imam* fingering. Triplet rhythm, *norm.* tone
F harmonic minor (two octaves), *mf*, *imam* fingering. Triplet rhythm, *norm.* tone
Bb major pentatonic (three octaves), *f*, *ma* fingering. Swing rhythm. *norm.* tone
F major pentatonic (two octaves), *f*, *ma* fingering. Swing rhythm. *norm.* tone

To be played *apoyando* and *legato*, with tone colour gradually changing from *norm.* to *pont.* to *norm.* again:

Bb natural minor (three octaves), *f*, *ma* fingering. Swing rhythm
F natural minor (two octaves), *f*, *ma* fingering. Swing rhythm

To be played *apoyando* and *legato*:

Bb melodic minor (three octaves), *p*, *im* fingering. Straight rhythm, *norm.* tone
F melodic minor (two octaves), *p*, *im* fingering. Straight rhythm, *tasto* tone

To be played *tirando* and *legato*, with tone colour gradually changing from *norm.* to *pont.* to *norm.* again:

Chromatic starting on Bb (three octaves), *mf*, *imam* fingering. Straight rhythm
Chromatic starting on F (two octaves), *mf*, *imam* fingering. Straight rhythm

To be played *apoyando* and *legato*; *dim.* ascending and *cresc.* descending:

Locrian starting on Bb (three octaves), *im* fingering. Triplet rhythm, *pont.* tone
Locrian starting on F (two octaves), *im* fingering. Triplet rhythm, *pont.* tone

Arpeggios (♩. = 100):

The following arpeggios to be performed *tirando* and *legato*:

Bb major (three octaves), *f*, *pont.* tone
F major (two octaves), *f*, *pont.* tone
Bb minor (three octaves), *p*, *norm.* tone
F minor (two octaves), *p*, *tasto* tone
Dominant 7th in the key of Eb (three octaves, starting on Bb); *cresc.* ascending, *dim.* descending
Dominant 7th in the key of Bb (two octaves, starting on F); *cresc.* ascending, *dim.* descending

The following arpeggios to be performed *tirando*, *staccato* and *mf*:

Diminished 7th starting on Bb (three octaves)
Diminished 7th starting on F (two octaves)

Exercises (♩ = 104):

The following exercises to be performed *tirando*, *legato* and *mf*:

F major scale in paired slurs (three octaves)
Bb major in 3rds (two octaves)
Bb major scale in 6ths (two octaves)
F minor scale in 10ths (two octaves)
Chromatic scale in octaves (two octaves, starting on F)

Bb major scale (three octaves)

F major scale (two octaves)

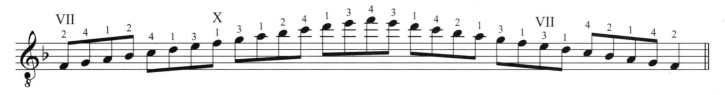

Bb harmonic minor scale (three octaves)

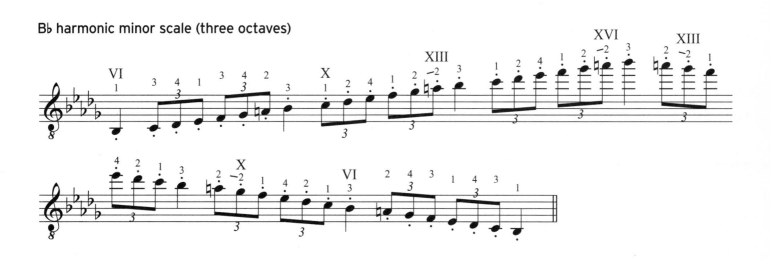

F harmonic minor scale (two octaves)

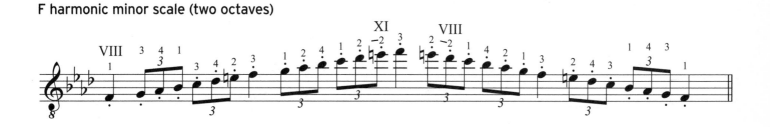

Guitar Grade 8 continued

Bb major pentatonic scale (three octaves)

F major pentatonic scale (two octaves)

Bb natural minor scale (three octaves)

F natural minor scale (two octaves)

Bb melodic minor scale (three octaves)

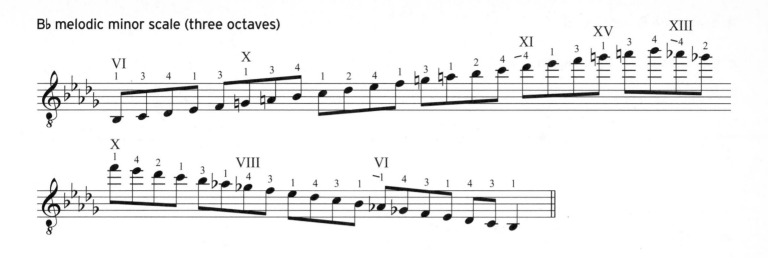

F melodic minor scale (two octaves)

Chromatic scale starting on Bb (three octaves)

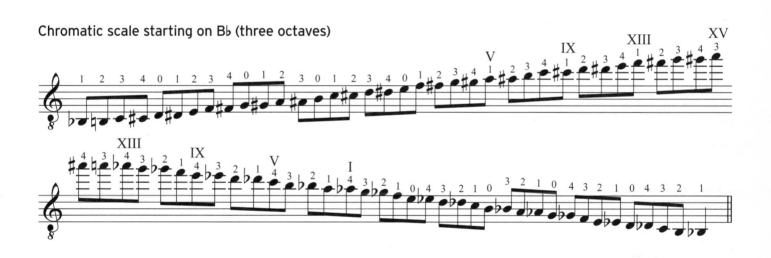

Chromatic scale starting on F (two octaves)

Guitar Grade 8 continued

Locrian scale on B♭ (three octaves)

Locrian scale on F (two octaves)

B♭ major arpeggio (three octaves)

F major arpeggio (two octaves)

B♭ minor arpeggio (three octaves)

F minor arpeggio (two octaves)

Dominant 7th arpeggio in the key of E♭ (three octaves)

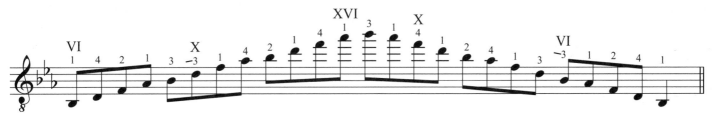

Dominant 7th arpeggio in the key of B♭ (two octaves)

Diminished 7th arpeggio starting on B♭ (three octaves)

Diminished 7th arpeggio starting on F (two octaves)

F major scale in paired slurs (three octaves)

Guitar Grade 8 continued

Bb major scale in 3rds (two octaves)

Bb major scale in 6ths (two octaves)

F major scale in 10ths (two octaves)

Chromatic scale in octaves starting on F (two octaves)

Plectrum Guitar Initial

Scales (♩ = 60):

The following scales to be performed from memory, *mf*, straight rhythm with alternate plectrum strokes:

C major (to 5th, ascending and descending)
G major (to 5th, ascending and descending)
D minor (to 5th, ascending and descending)

Arpeggios (♩ = 60):

The following arpeggios to be performed from memory, *mf*, straight rhythm with alternate plectrum strokes:

C major (to 5th, ascending and descending)

G major (to 5th, ascending and descending)

D minor (to 5th, ascending and descending)

C major scale (to 5th)

G major scale (to 5th)

D minor scale (to 5th)

C major arpeggio (to 5th)

G major arpeggio (to 5th)

D minor arpeggio (to 5th)

Plectrum Guitar Grade 1

Scales (♩ = 72):

The following scales to be performed from memory, *mf*, straight rhythm with alternate plectrum strokes:

C major (one octave)
G major (one octave)
A natural minor (one octave)

Arpeggios (♩ = 72):

The following arpeggios to be performed from memory, *mf*, straight rhythm with plectrum strokes as shown*:

C major (one octave)
G major (one octave)
A minor (one octave)

Chord Sequence

I-V^7-I in C major

C major scale (one octave)

G major scale (one octave)

A natural minor scale (one octave)

C major arpeggio (one octave)

* ⊓ = Downstroke

  V = Upstroke

G major arpeggio (one octave)

A minor arpeggio (one octave)

I-V^7-I chord sequence in C major

Plectrum Guitar Grade 2

Scales (♩ = 88):

The following scales to be performed from memory; straight rhythm with alternate plectrum strokes, ***p*** or ***f***, as requested by the examiner:

D major - open (one octave)
D major - closed (one octave)
B♭ major (one octave)
E harmonic minor (two octaves)
A jazz melodic minor (two octaves)

Arpeggios (♩ = 88):

The following arpeggio to be performed from memory; straight rhythm with alternate plectrum strokes, ***p*** or ***f***, as requested by the examiner:

D major (one octave)

Broken Chords (♩ = 88):

The following broken chords to be performed from memory; straight rhythm with plectrum strokes as shown, ***p*** or ***f***, as requested by the examiner:

E minor (two octaves)
A minor (range of a 12th)

Chord Sequences (♩ = 88):

II-V⁷-I in C major
II-V-I in D major

D major scale - open (one octave)

D major scale - closed (one octave)

B♭ major scale (one octave)

E harmonic minor scale (two octaves)

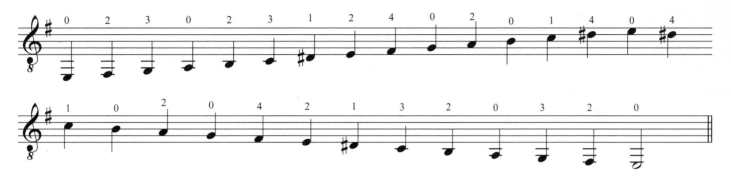

A jazz melodic minor scale (two octaves)

D major arpeggio (one octave)

E minor broken chord (two octaves)

A minor broken chord (range of a 12th)

Plectrum Guitar Grade 2 continued

Chord Sequence in C major

Chord Sequence in D major

Plectrum Guitar Grade 3

Scales (♩ = 60):

The following scales to be performed from memory, with alternate plectrum strokes; straight or swung rhythm (with the following rhythm for each octave of the scale: ♩ ♩♪ ♪♩ ♪), ***p*** or ***f***, as requested by the examiner:

C major (two octaves)

A major (two octaves)

B harmonic minor (two octaves)

G melodic minor (two octaves)

G pentatonic major (two octaves)

Arpeggios (♩ = 60):

The following arpeggio to be performed from memory; straight rhythm with plectrum strokes as shown, ***p*** or ***f***, as requested by the examiner:

C major (two octaves)

Exercises:

The following exercises to be performed from memory; ***p*** or ***f***, as requested by the examiner:

1. B♭ major – Ascending slurs, straight or swung rhythm (♫ = ♪³♪) (♩ = 60)

2. G minor – Half barré study (♩. = 60)

Chord Sequence

II-V^7-I in G major

C major scale (two octaves)

A major scale (two octaves)

B harmonic minor scale (two octaves)

Plectrum Guitar Grade 3 continued

G melodic minor scale (two octaves)

G pentatonic major scale (two octaves)

C major arpeggio (two octaves)

Exercise: B♭ major – Ascending slurs

Exercise: G minor – Half barré study

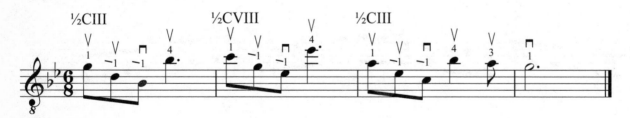

Chord Sequence in G major

Plectrum Guitar Grade 4

Scales (♩ = 68)

The following scales to be performed from memory, with alternate plectrum strokes; straight or swung rhythm (♩ ♪ = ♪³♪ ♪³♪ ♪³♪), **p** or **f**, as requested by the examiner:

E major - open (two octaves)
E major - closed (two octaves)
A natural minor (two octaves)
F♯ harmonic minor (two octaves)

Arpeggios (♩ = 68)

The following arpeggio to be performed from memory; straight rhythm and plectrum strokes as shown; **p** or **f**, as requested by the examiner:

Dominant 7th in the key of A (two octaves)

Exercises

The following exercises to be performed from memory; **p**, **mf** or **f**, as requested by the examiner:

F major - IV-V-I (♩. = 52)
D major - Ascending slurs (♩ = 68)
F♯ minor - Half barré study (♩. = 52)

Chord Sequence

D major-B⁷-Em⁷-A⁷ (♩. = 70)

E major scale - open (two octaves)

E major scale - closed (two octaves)

A natural minor (two octaves)

Plectrum Guitar Grade 4 continued

F# harmonic minor scale (two octaves)

Dominant 7th arpeggio in the key of A (two octaves)

Exercise: F major – IV–V–I

Exercise: D major – Ascending slurs

Exercise: F# minor – Half barré study

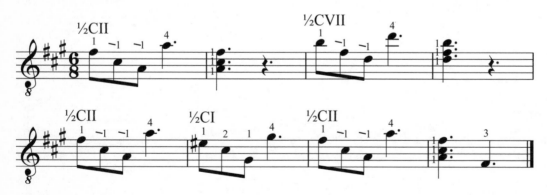

Chord Sequence: D major–B⁷–Em⁷–A⁷

Plectrum Guitar Grade 5

Scales (♩ = 80):

The following scales to be performed from memory, with alternate plectrum strokes; straight or swung rhythm (♩ $\overset{3}{\sqcap}$ ♪♩ $\overset{3}{\sqcap}$ ♪♩ $\overset{3}{\sqcap}$ ♪), **p**, **mf** or **f**, as requested by the examiner:

B major (two octaves)
G natural minor (two octaves)
F harmonic minor (two octaves)
F melodic minor (two octaves)
E dorian (two octaves)

Arpeggios (♩ = 80):

The following arpeggio to be performed from memory; straight rhythm, **p**, **mf** or **f**, as requested by the examiner:

Diminished 7th starting and finishing on C (two octaves)

Exercises

The following exercises to be performed from memory; **p**, **mf** or **f**, as requested by the examiner:

I-VI-II-V⁷-I in G major (♩. = 56)
A major - paired slurs, straight or swung rhythm (♫ = $\overset{3}{\sqcap}$ ♪) (♩ = 80)

Chord Sequence

F#m⁷-Bm⁷-Em⁹-A⁷ (♩ = 80)

B major scale (two octaves)

G natural minor scale (two octaves)

F harmonic minor scale (two octaves)

Plectrum Guitar Grade 5 continued

F melodic minor scale (two octaves)

E dorian scale (two octaves)

Diminished 7th arpeggio on C (two octaves)

Exercise: I–VI–II–V⁷–I in G major

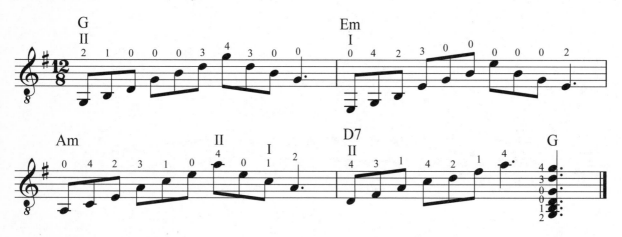

Exercise: A major – paired slurs

Chord Sequence: F#m⁷–Bm⁷–Em⁹–A⁷

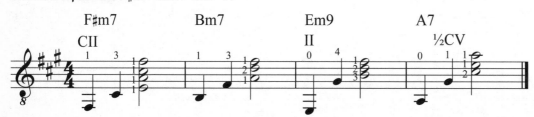

Plectrum Guitar Grade 6

Scales (♩ = 92):

The following scales to be performed from memory; straight or swung rhythm (♩ = ♩³♪ ♩³♪ ♩³♪ ♩³♪), p, mf or f, as requested by the examiner:

A major (three octaves)
E major (three octaves)
G major (two octaves)
E♭ major (two octaves)
A harmonic minor (three octaves)
A melodic minor (three octaves)
A jazz melodic minor (three octaves)
C harmonic minor (two octaves)
C melodic minor (two octaves)
C dorian (two octaves)

Arpeggios (♩ = 60):

The following arpeggios to be performed from memory; straight rhythm, p, mf or f, as requested by the examiner:

E major (three octaves)
F major (three octaves)
E♭ major (two octaves)
E minor (three octaves)
F minor (three octaves)
C minor (two octaves)
Dominant 7th in E major, starting and finishing on B (two octaves)
D major 7th (range of a 12th)

Cadences

The following cadences to be performed from memory; p, mf or f as requested by the examiner:

II-V⁷-I in C major (two versions)
I-VI-II-V progression in B♭ major

A major scale (three octaves) – see Classical Guitar Grade 7

E major scale (three octaves)

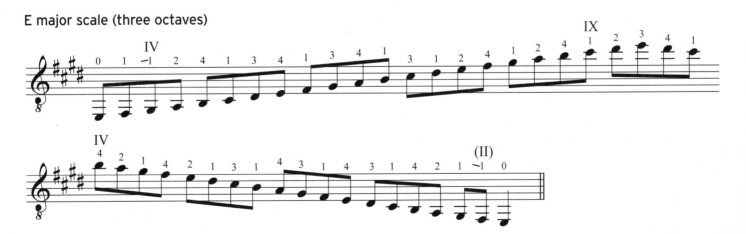

Plectrum Guitar Grade 6 continued

G major scale (two octaves)

E♭ major scale (two octaves)

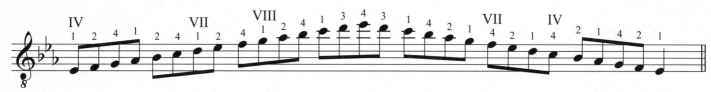

A harmonic minor scale (three octaves)

A melodic minor scale (three octaves)

A jazz melodic minor scale (three octaves)

C harmonic minor scale (two octaves)

C melodic minor scale (two octaves)

Dorian scale on C (two octaves)

E major arpeggio (three octaves)

Plectrum Guitar Grade 6 continued

F major arpeggio (three octaves)

E♭ major arpeggio (two octaves)

E minor arpeggio (three octaves)

F minor arpeggio (three octaves)

C minor arpeggio (two octaves) - see Classical Guitar Grade 6

Dominant 7th arpeggio in E major (two octaves), starting and finishing on B

D major 7th arpeggio (range of a 12th)

Cadence in C major (1)

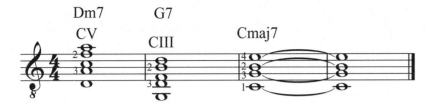

Cadence in C major (2)

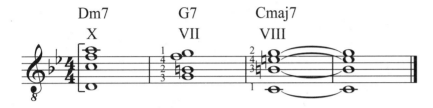

Progression in Bb major

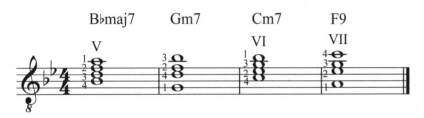

Plectrum Guitar Grade 7

Both sections i) and ii) to be performed from memory; *p*, *mf* or *f*, straight or swung rhythm (♩ = 𝄇³𝄇³𝄇³𝄇³), as requested by the examiner.

Scales (♩ = 118) and arpeggios (♩ = 90):

The following scales and arpeggios are to be prepared, based on **one** of the two pairs of tonal/modal centres:

either **Group 1:**

E (three octaves, except where specified)

E♭ (two octaves)

or **Group 2:**

G (three octaves, except where specified)

C (two octaves)

The major scale

The harmonic minor scale

The melodic minor scale

The mixolydian scale (two octaves only)

The blues scale (two octaves only)

The major arpeggio (straight rhythm only)

The minor arpeggio (straight rhythm only)

The dominant 7th starting and finishing on the selected tonal centres (e.g. starting on E to form the dominant 7th of the key of A)

A major 7th (range of a 12th) is also to be prepared

Cadences

II-V-I progression in E♭ major, G major and C minor

I-VI-II-V-I progression in F major

E major scale (three octaves) - see Plectrum Guitar Grade 6

E harmonic minor scale (three octaves)

E melodic minor scale (three octaves)

Mixolydian scale on E (two octaves)

Blues scale on E (two octaves)

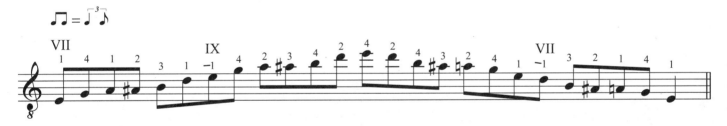

E major arpeggio (three octaves) – see Plectrum Guitar Grade 6

E minor arpeggio (three octaves) – see Plectrum Guitar Grade 6

Dominant 7th arpeggio on E (three octaves)

Eb major scale (two octaves) – see Plectrum Guitar Grade 6

Plectrum Guitar Grade 7 continued

E♭ harmonic minor scale (two octaves)

E♭ melodic minor scale (two octaves)

Mixolydian scale on E♭ (two octaves)

Blues scale on E♭ (two octaves)

E♭ major arpeggio (two octaves) – see Plectrum Guitar Grade 6

E♭ minor arpeggio (two octaves)

Dominant 7th arpeggio on E♭ (two octaves)

G major scale (three octaves) - see Guitar Grade 6

G harmonic minor scale (three octaves)

G melodic minor scale (three octaves)

Mixolydian scale on G (two octaves)

Blues scale on G (two octaves)

G major arpeggio (three octaves) - see Classical Guitar Grade 6

G minor arpeggio (three octaves) - see Classical Guitar Grade 6

Plectrum Guitar Grade 7 continued

Dominant 7th arpeggio on G (two octaves)

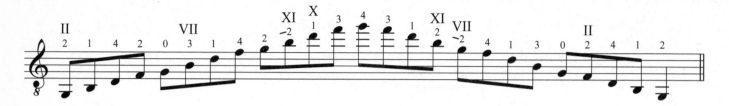

C major scale (two octaves) – see Plectrum Guitar Grade 3

C harmonic minor scale (two octaves) – see Plectrum Guitar Grade 6

C melodic minor scale (two octaves) – see Plectrum Guitar Grade 6

Mixolydian scale on C (two octaves)

Blues scale on C (two octaves)

C major arpeggio (two octaves) – see Plectrum Guitar Grade 3

C minor arpeggio (two octaves) – see Plectrum Guitar Grade 6

Dominant 7th arpeggio on C (two octaves)

54

A major 7th arpeggio (to a 12th)

Cadence in E♭ major II-V-I

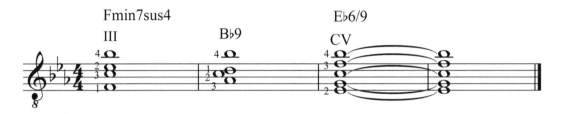

Cadence in G major II-V-I

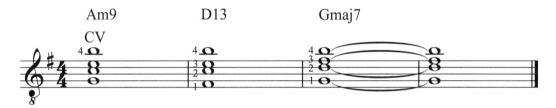

Cadence in C minor II-V-I

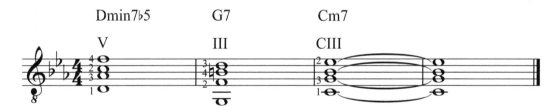

Progression in F major I-VI-II-V-I

Plectrum Guitar Grade 8

Both sections i) and ii) to be performed from memory; straight or swung rhythm (♩ ♪♪ ♪♪ ♪♪), **p**, **mf** or **f**, as requested by the examiner.

Scales (♩ = 132) **and arpeggios** (♩ = 100):

The following scales and arpeggios are to be prepared, based on **one** of the two pairs of tonal/modal centres:

either **Group 1:**

F (three octaves, except where specified)

F♯ (two octaves)

or **Group 2:**

B♭ (three octaves, except where specified)

D (two octaves)

The major scale

The harmonic minor scale

The melodic minor scale

The jazz melodic minor

The pentatonic major scale (two octaves only)

The major arpeggio (straight rhythm only)

The minor arpeggio (straight rhythm only)

The dominant 7th starting and finishing on the selected tonal centres (e.g. starting on F to form the dominant 7th of the key of B♭)

The following are also to be prepared:

Diminished 7th starting and finishing on E (two octaves)

D minor 7th (range of a 12th)

Cadences

II-V-I progression in A major, D♭ major, and C♯ minor

I-VI-II-V-I progression in C major and G major

F major scale (three octaves)

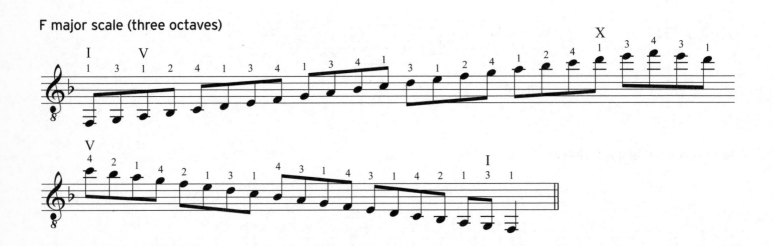

F harmonic minor scale (three octaves)

F melodic minor scale (three octaves)

F jazz melodic minor scale (three octaves)

F pentatonic major scale (two octaves)

Plectrum Guitar Grade 8 continued

F major arpeggio (three octaves) – see Plectrum Guitar Grade 6

F minor arpeggio (three octaves) – see Plectrum Guitar Grade 6

Dominant 7th arpeggio on F (three octaves)

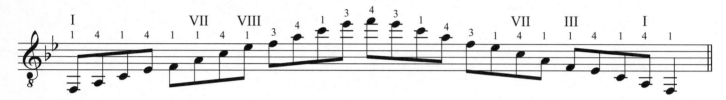

F# major scale (two octaves)

F# harmonic minor scale (two octaves)

F# melodic minor scale (two octaves)

F# jazz melodic minor scale (two octaves)

F♯ pentatonic major scale (two octaves)

F♯ major arpeggio (two octaves)

F♯ minor arpeggio (two octaves)

Dominant 7th arpeggio on F♯ (two octaves)

B♭ major scale (three octaves) – see Classical Guitar Grade 8

B♭ harmonic minor scale (three octaves)

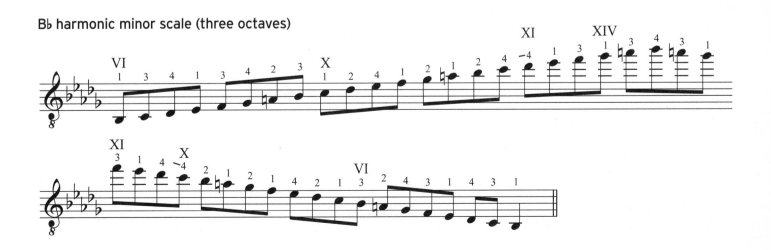

Plectrum Guitar Grade 8 continued

Bb melodic minor scale (three octaves)

Bb jazz melodic minor scale (three octaves)

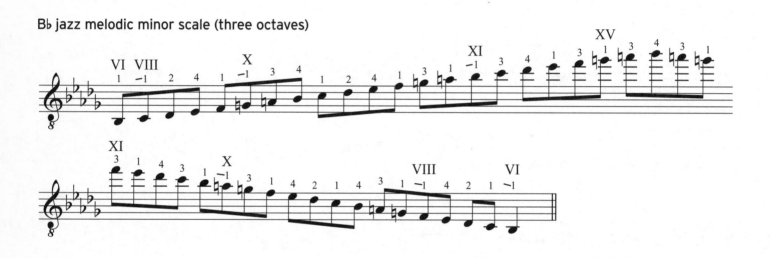

Bb pentatonic major scale (two octaves)

Bb major arpeggio (three octaves) – see Classical Guitar Grade 8

Bb minor arpeggio (three octaves) – see Classical Guitar Grade 8

Dominant 7th arpeggio on Bb (three octaves) – see Classical Guitar Grade 8

D major scale (two octaves) – see Classical Guitar Grade 7

D harmonic minor scale (two octaves)

D melodic minor scale (two octaves)

D jazz melodic minor scale (two octaves)

D pentatonic major scale (two octaves)

D major arpeggio (two octaves) – see Classical Guitar Grade 7

D minor arpeggio (two octaves) – see Classical Guitar Grade 7

Dominant 7th arpeggio on D (two octaves) – see Classical Guitar Grade 7

Diminished 7th arpeggio on E (two octaves)

D minor 7th arpeggio (range of a 12th)

Plectrum Guitar Grade 8 continued

Cadence in A major II-V-I

Cadence in Db major II-V-I

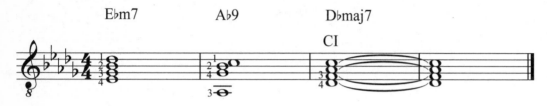

Cadence in C# minor II-V-I

Progression in C major

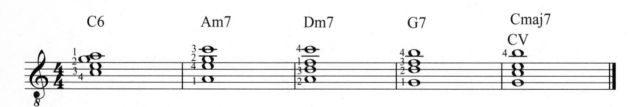

Progression in G major

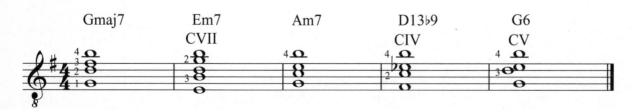